THIS
BOOK
BELONGS

TO _____

GROLIER
B O O K S

DISNEY'S
SMALL WORLD LIBRARY
GOOFY JOINS THE CIRCUS
An Adventure in Russia

Developed by The Walt Disney Company in conjunction with Nancy Hall, Inc.
ISBN: 0-7172-8219-8
Grolier Books is a division of Grolier Enterprises, Inc.

"Gawrsh!" said Goofy. "Moscow sure is a pretty city!"
Mickey, Minnie, Goofy, Morty, and Ferdie were
visiting Moscow, the capital of Russia. They were riding
through a part of town known as Red Square, when
Mickey asked the taxi driver to stop.

"This looks like a good place to take some pictures,"
he said.

"Look at the building over there!" cried Morty.

"It looks like a fairy-tale castle," said Minnie.

"That's St. Basil's Cathedral," Mickey explained, glancing at his guidebook, "and that's the Kremlin. It says here that the Kremlin is filled with special paintings, called icons, and golden treasures from long ago."

Their next stop was Gorky Park, a huge public park in the center of Moscow. Mickey and Minnie went for a ride on a boat with Morty and Ferdie while Goofy rode the giant Ferris wheel.

When they got off the ride, they joined Goofy for a stroll through the park. All around them were flowers and fountains and people playing chess.

"Look!" cried Morty. "There's some kind of show over there."

He ran over and asked a man what was going on.

"It's a juggling contest," the man said. "The winner gets to perform with the Moscow Circus when it goes to St. Petersburg."

"Imagine that!" exclaimed Minnie. "The Moscow Circus is one of the most famous circuses in the world."

"Gawrsh!" exclaimed Goofy, his eyes glued to one of the performers. "Look at how many rings she has in the air at once. That sure looks like fun."

Each juggler was better than the one before. Then Goofy noticed some clowns juggling balls while riding unicycles.

One clown kept pretending to fall, but he always managed to catch himself just in time.

"Why is he dropping all those balls?" asked Morty as, one by one, the balls flew into the audience.

"It's just part of the act," said Mickey. "He's got lots more to juggle."

But Goofy was eagerly waiting for his chance to help out.

"I'll catch them for you!" he shouted. And with that, he danced toward the clown, catching the falling balls and tossing them back again. The crowd began to laugh. Goofy was a hit! His timing was perfect, and he didn't miss a single ball.

When the last ball flew far from where he was standing, Goofy dived to catch it in his hat. By this time, the crowd was roaring with laughter. Everyone began to clap.

"Gawrsh, thanks!" said Goofy as he took a bow. The crowd went wild.

"You've won the contest!" cried the ringmaster.

"Me?" said Goofy. "I was just having fun. I'm no juggler. Tell him, Mickey!"

"Why?" Mickey asked. "You were terrific. And we can all go to St. Petersburg to watch you perform."

"Great! Then come with me," said the ringmaster excitedly. "There are some people I'd like you to meet."

The ringmaster took Goofy to the circus hall, where he introduced Goofy to two jugglers named Andrei and Tanya. The jugglers showed Goofy around and took him to meet other performers.

Katerina, the trapeze artist, was practicing part of her act.

"I am so happy to meet you, Goofy," she called down. "I hear you are quite a juggler."

"Gawrsh, I don't know about that," replied Goofy, blushing. "But I'm going to try my best."

"I'm sure you'll be terrific," said Katerina.

Goofy began to get nervous. "What if I can't juggle?" he thought to himself. "What if they boo me off the stage?"

Andrei and Tanya took Goofy to meet Misha, the animal trainer.

Misha handed several clubs to two bears and beamed proudly as they began to juggle them.

"Oh, no!" Goofy said to himself, even more worried. "Even the bears can juggle better than I can!"

Then the loud trumpeting of an elephant made Goofy forget all about juggling.

"Come meet Natasha," said Misha, leading Goofy to the elephant's cage. "She's quite a performer. But I can't wait to see your act," he continued. "I hear you're quite a performer, too."

Goofy got even more nervous. He fainted into a big pile of Natasha's hay.

Natasha didn't want anyone taking a nap in her hay. She woke Goofy up with a trunk full of water!

"Wh-wh-where am I?" stammered Goofy.

"You're still at the circus," said Misha, laughing. "But you should probably get some rest. I'll show you to your dressing room."

Goofy had a very bad case of stage fright. "I don't feel very well," he said, clutching his stomach. "Maybe I shouldn't juggle after all."

"Don't worry," said Misha. "We'll help you feel better in no time."

Katerina fed Goofy some borscht, a Russian soup. Alexi, the clown, gave him some thin pancakes called blinis, served with caviar, a Russian delicacy of fish eggs. Andrei and Tanya gave him tea with honey.

Goofy was starting to feel a little better.

"I have a confession to make," he said. "I'm not really a juggler."

"That's all right, Goofy," replied Olga, the acrobat, kindly. "Don't be nervous. You're going to do just fine."

Goofy felt a little more cheerful in the morning.

It was fun being part of the circus, he decided. There was so much to do and see. He had new friends, and his old friends were here, too. Best of all, new friends and old were going to St. Petersburg on the circus train together!

They all arrived in St. Petersburg on a beautiful sunny morning.

"You must let me take you and your friends to see some of the sights of this wonderful city," said Tanya to Goofy and his friends. "Let's begin with the Summer Palace of Czar Peter I, who ruled our country for many years. The hydrofoil will get us there in no time."

"What's a hydrofoil?" asked Morty.

"You'll see," said Tanya, as she led everyone to a dock.
Everyone climbed aboard a strange-looking boat.
Slowly the vehicle pulled away from the dock. Then
suddenly, as it picked up speed, it rose out of the water.

"Gawrsh!" said Goofy. "How did we do that?"

"We're riding on special water wings. The trip will be
very fast and very smooth," explained Tanya.

"Peter the Great was one of the most powerful rulers in history," Tanya told Goofy and his friends. "He spared no expense when he had this palace built for himself and his wife, Catherine I."

"I've never seen anything so grand!" said Minnie.

Later, when they were touring the grounds, Goofy discovered the trick fountains.

"You need to have perfect timing to avoid getting wet," said Tanya.

But it was too late. Goofy was already soaked.

"I sure hope my timing is better than this during the show," Goofy said to himself.

That night Tanya and Andrei invited everyone to see the Kirov Ballet. Inside the building the twinkling lights from crystal chandeliers made everything glow.

Suddenly, the lights dimmed and the music began. No one said a word as the dancers performed the ballet of Swan Lake. When it was over, Goofy stood up to applaud. He couldn't help but notice how proud and happy the dancers looked as they took their final bows.

"I'll do my very best tomorrow night," Goofy said to himself. "Then everyone will stand up and clap for me, too!"

Goofy woke up early the next morning and began to practice. By the time of the show, he was ready. Goofy waited to hear the lively, funny music. Then he ran out into the center ring.

The audience watched as Goofy did crazy flips and somersaults while he juggled balls and then rings. Then Goofy took his eyes off the rings for a minute, and they began to slip right over his head and down past his shoulders one by one.

"It's mighty hard to juggle this way, folks!" said Goofy, whose arms were now clamped close to his body. Before he knew it, there wasn't one ring left in the air!

The crowd stood up and chanted his name.

"Goofy! Goofy! Goofy!" they cried.

Goofy stood there proudly and took one bow after another.

"Gawrsh!" he said. "I had no idea I was this good!"

"You were great!" said Mickey, running up to congratulate him.

"Well, I tried as hard as I could," said Goofy. "And that's the most important thing!"

Did You Know...?

Every country has many different customs and places that make it special. Some of the things that make Russia special are mentioned below. Do you recognize any of them from the story?

The Kremlin is a walled area within the city of Moscow, which is the capital of Russia. It was once a mighty fort, but now visitors from all over the world come to see the beautiful old palaces, cathedrals, and museums it contains.

Red Square in Moscow isn't really red at all. Its name comes from an old Russian word that means "red," but also means "beautiful." On holidays people come into the huge square to watch parades and celebrate.

Trained bears have been entertaining Russians for hundreds of years in circuses and other places. They are taught to juggle, dance, and perform all sorts of tricks.

Moscow's Gorky Park has something for everyone. Besides a big amusement park, Gorky Park has tennis courts, ice skating rinks, and an outdoor theater.

St. Petersburg is built on 101 islands that are connected by bridges. Many people consider St. Petersburg the most beautiful city in the country.

Peter the Great, the Russian *czar* (ZAR), or emperor, had the city of St. Petersburg built. Peter had many talents, and he was a skilled carpenter, blacksmith, tailor, and drummer.

The summer palace of Peter the Great still stands outside St. Petersburg. It is famous for its beautiful gardens and fountains. Many of the fountains turn on and off at different times, playing tricks on unsuspecting visitors.

Russia is well known for its dancers. Many cities have their own ballet companies, and folk dancing is enjoyed everywhere. Each region has its own folk dances and colorful folk costumes.

Caviar is a favorite special food in Russia. This delicacy is actually the salted eggs of fish. The most expensive caviar can cost up to hundreds of dollars for a pound or less!

"Zdravstvuyte!" (ZDRAHAT-vooyt-eh) means "Hello" in the Russian language.